Treasure Island

Robert Louis Stevenson

STUDENT PACKET

NOTE:

The trade book edition of the novel used to prepare this guide is found in the Novel Units catalog and on the Novel Units website. Using other editions may have varied page references.

Please note: We have assigned Interest Levels based on our knowledge of the themes and ideas of the books included in the Novel Units sets, however, please assess the appropriateness of this novel or trade book for the age level and maturity of your students prior to reading with them. You know your students best!

ISBN 978-1-58130-754-2

To order, contact your
local school supply store, or:

Toll-Free Fax: 877.716.7272
Phone: 888.650.4224
3901 Union Blvd., Suite 155
St. Louis, MO 63115

sales@novelunits.com

novelunits.com

Name _____

Storytelling

Part 1

Directions: Brainstorm all of the necessary parts of a story on an attribute web. Then, sort the story elements into categories.

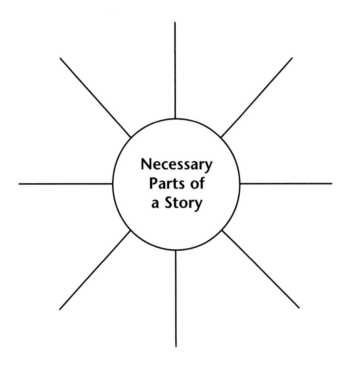

Part 2

Directions: Read the first paragraph of the novel. Judging from this paragraph and the information on the cover of the book, predict how you think *Treasure Island* will address the major components of a story (brainstormed above).

Directions: Freewrite about the following ideas. Predict how all of the elements will work together to form the story *Treasure Island*.

1. buccaneer

2. treasure

3. mutiny

4. captain

5. bravery

6. fear

Part One, "The Old Buccaneer," pp. 11-46

1. Where does the narrator live as he begins to tell the story?
2. Why does the new lodger choose to stay at the Admiral Benbow?
3. For what job does the guest pay the narrator?
4. How do the country people react to the guest's stories?
5. How does the doctor treat the guest?
6. How does the person looking for Bill treat the narrator?
7. What happens as a result of the conversation between Black Dog and the captain?
8. What does the captain confess to Jim? What does he want Jim to do?
9. What is the captain afraid of?
10. What happens the same night the captain confesses to Jim?
11. Who comes to the Admiral Benbow after the funeral takes place?
12. What does the blind man give to the captain?
13. What does the captain do? How does Jim react?
14. What do Jim and his mother do after the captain dies?
15. Who returns to the inn while Jim and his mother are there? What do Jim and his mother do?
16. What happens at the Admiral Benbow while Jim and his mother are by the bridge?
17. Who arrives on horseback?
18. Why does Jim want to see Dr. Livesey?
19. What is in the oilskin bag?
20. What do the three decide to do? What is the doctor worried about?

Part Two, "The Sea-cook," pp. 47-80

1. What does Jim dream about?
2. Summarize the contents of Trelawney's letter to Dr. Livesey and Jim.
3. How does Jim feel the last day he spends at the Admiral Benbow?
4. What was Jim's first impression of Long John Silver from the squire's letter? What is his impression when he first meets him?
5. What does Captain Smollett report to the squire and doctor when they, along with Jim, board the *Hispaniola*? What does the doctor think?

6. What do the squire and Jim think of Captain Smollett?

7. What does Jim reveal about Arrow?

8. What does Jim overhear while in the apple barrel?

9. What saves Jim from being discovered in the barrel?

10. What does Jim do with his new information?

11. What do Jim and the others decide to do?

12. What task is Jim given?

Part Three, "My Shore Adventure," pp. 81-98

1. How does the men's countenance change as they approach land?

2. What is decided at the council held in the cabin?

3. How are the men divided to go ashore? What does Jim do?

4. Why does Jim feel he is neglecting his duties after he is ashore?

5. What happens in the hidden part of the marsh?

6. What does Long John do to Tom? Why?

7. How does Jim react to what he has witnessed?

8. Who chases Jim in the woods?

9. What makes Jim think he has found an ally?

10. About what does Ben Gunn inquire?

11. What makes Jim start running again?

Part Four, "The Stockade," pp. 99-130

1. Who narrates this section of the book? What do you think about the narrator's voice changing?

2. What is the doctor's impression of the anchorage?

3. What do the doctor and Hunter decide to do?

4. Why does the doctor decide to return to the ship and what does he learn?

5. What is their next course of action?

6. What provisions are loaded into the boat?

7. What do the men forget about on the *Hispaniola*?

8. Who was Flint's gunner?

9. What happens to the jolly-boat? What is lost?

10. Who is the first of the honest men to die in battle? How is he treated?

11. What effect does the cannonade have on the men in the stockade?

12. How does Jim find his friends?

13. What is the Jolly Roger?

14. In what state do Captain Smollett and his men find themselves? Explain.

15. What do they decide on as a plan of action?

16. How does Captain Smollett initially react to Silver's appearance the next morning?

17. Why does Silver say he is asking for a truce? Who does Jim think is responsible for Silver's claims about Captain Smollett and his men?

18. What are the terms of Silver's truce? Does Smollett choose to accept it? Would you? Why or why not?

19. What are Captain Smollett's terms of truce? How does Silver respond?

20. Why is the captain angry?

21. From what position do the buccaneers make their attack?

22. How many are left standing and able to fight on both sides after the attack?

23. **Prediction:** What is the outcome of the attack?

Part Five, "My Sea Adventure," pp. 131-166

1. What happens to the men wounded in battle?

2. Where does Jim suspect the doctor is going after talking with the captain and squire?

3. What does Jim decide to do?

4. What is the coracle? How well does it work?

5. Who is on the *Hispaniola* as Jim approaches?

6. Does Jim succeed in his plans?

7. What is the state of the men aboard the ship?

8. What does Jim announce to Hands after getting him some brandy? What does he do that symbolizes his claim?

9. What bargain do Israel Hands and Jim make?

10. What does Hands ask for with a slight hesitation?

11. What does Jim discover while he is supposed to be getting wine?

12. Why does Hands plead for Jim to cut him a quid of tobacco?

13. What are the two different views Jim and Israel Hands hold about the dead?

14. Why doesn't Jim's gun work the first time he shoots at Hands?

15. What does Hands do with his dirk after Jim reloads his guns?

16. What happens next?

17. How does Jim feel as he pushes the man in the red cap overboard?

18. What makes Jim feel like something went wrong while he was away?

19. Who cries loudly as Jim enters the little block house?

20. **Prediction:** Will Jim survive after the buccaneers discover who he is?

Part Six, "Captain Silver," pp. 167-211

1. How many buccaneers are still alive?

2. What does Long John reveal about Jim's friends? Do you believe Long John? Why or why not?

3. What does Jim want to know? How does Long John respond?

4. What does Jim reveal about himself in his monologue on pages 170-171?

5. Who tries to kill Jim? What happens?

6. What do the men ask their captain to allow them to do? Does he allow it?

7. What does Long John tell Jim?

8. What do Long John's men give him? Where did it come from?

9. What are the rules of order for being deposed by a black spot?

10. What are the four grievances of the crew?

11. How does Long John respond to the crew? What does the crew decide after hearing his responses?

12. What does Jim notice about the doctor's way of relating to Silver's men?

13. Why do the men oppose Silver's agreement to let Jim talk to the doctor? Are their reasons sound?

14. Describe Jim's conversation with the doctor.

15. What does the doctor promise Silver?

16. Why is the doctor promising to help Silver?

17. What does Silver tell his crew during breakfast?

18. What does Jim feel during breakfast?

19. What do the men look for first as they seek the treasure?

20. What do they find at the base of a tree? What is peculiar about it? Why is it peculiar?

21. Who do the men think is calling, "Darby McGraw" at first? Who is it really?

22. Why are the men disappointed at the end of Chapter 32?

23. What happened to the treasure?

24. What do Jim and the others do with the treasure? What do they do with the three men remaining of Silver's crew?

25. What happens to Silver?

26. What happens to those who remained on the ship?

bearings (11)	year of grace (11)	tarry (11)	livid (11)
grog-shop (12)	diabolical (13)	assizes (16)	cutlass (18)
hilt (19)	lee (24)	apoplexy (29)	reiterated (37)
miscreant (38)	prodigiously (43)	rum-puncheon (43)	plundered (45)
incomprehensible (46)			

Directions: Choose the word that does NOT belong in each group. Be prepared to explain your choices.

1. bearings	situation	gears	direction
2. year of grace	calendar year	year of mercy	Christian calendar
3. tarry	hurry	wait	delay
4. livid	pallid	vibrant	dull
5. grog shop	tearoom	bar	alcohol
6. diabolical	scrupulous	devilish	roguish
7. assizes	courts	trials	gallows
8. cutlass	jewelry	sword	machete
9. hilt	edge	handle	grip
10. lee	covered	cleared	sheltered
11. apoplexy	stroke	blood clot	caress
12. reiterated	recorded	redundant	repeated
13. miscreant	infidel	illegitimate	criminal
14. prodigiously	proudly	enormously	extraordinarily
15. rum-puncheon	barrel	cask	left-hook
16. plundered	looted	stormed	pillaged
17. incomprehensible	unbelievable	impossible	understandable

calumnies (49) odious (49) coxswain (72) forecastle (72)
chapling (73) pannikin (74) mizzen-top (75) fore-sail (75)
careen (76) duplicity (77) prodigious (80)

Directions: Form a group with four other students. Study the example below. Then, assign the remaining words so that each group member has two. Fill out a word map for each word, defining them according to how they were used in the book. Share your completed word maps with the class.

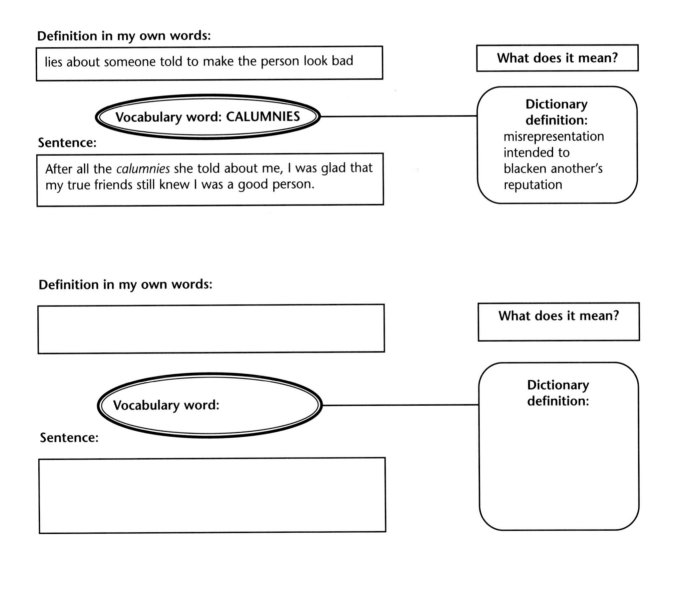

Definition in my own words:

lies about someone told to make the person look bad

What does it mean?

Vocabulary word: CALUMNIES

Dictionary definition: misrepresentation intended to blacken another's reputation

Sentence:

After all the *calumnies* she told about me, I was glad that my true friends still knew I was a good person.

Definition in my own words:

What does it mean?

Vocabulary word:

Dictionary definition:

Sentence:

scuppers (82)   undulating (86)   desperadoes (88)   extricate (90)
apparition (92)   nondescript (92)   dysentery (99)   abominable (99)
gallipot (104)   tarpaulin (105)   palisade (109)   acquiesce (110)
close hauled (111) cannonade (115)   doldrums (126)

Directions: Use the clues on this page to complete the crossword puzzle below.

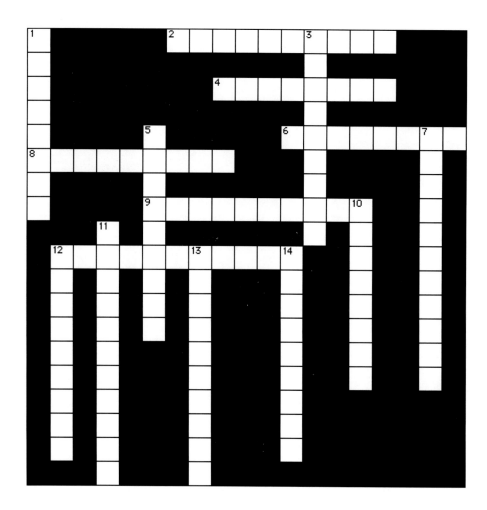

Down

1. several openings on a ship's bulwark through which water from the deck can flow overboard
3. protective piece of material
5. passively accept
7. bold criminals
10. small, ceramic vessel
11. unidentifiable object
12. bombardment
13. detestable
14. disease usually caused by infection

Across

2. an unusual or unexpected sight
4. calm area in the ocean near the equator
6. defensive fence made of stakes
8. to remove from an entanglement
9. wavy
12. sailing as much against the wind as possible (two words)

Name _____

apoplectic (131)   coracle (136)   hawser (137)   impulsion (139)
phosphorescent (140)   reverberations (142)   contrariety (143)   promontory (144)
yawing (146)   volition (160)   kelson (170)   plucky (174)
gibbet (178)   ambiguity (191)   volubly (196)   dereliction (205)
supplication (209)   connived (210)

Directions: Match each word to the best definition.

_____ 1. apoplectic   a. brave

_____ 2. coracle   b. a large rope for securing a ship

_____ 3. hawser   c. swerving, weaving

_____ 4. impulsion   d. opposition

_____ 5. phosphorescent   e. abandonment

_____ 6. reverberations   f. gallows

_____ 7. contrariety   g. conspired

_____ 8. promontory   h. timber on a ship intended to strengthen the structure

_____ 9. yawing   i. small, hide-covered boat

_____10. volition   j. echoing sounds

_____11. kelson   k. high point of land or rock

_____12. plucky   l. humble entreaty; prayer

_____13. gibbet   m. showing stroke symptoms

_____14. ambiguity   n. obscurity; uncertainty

_____15. volubly   o. luminescent

_____16. dereliction   p. decision-making process; will

_____17. supplication   q. rapidly, as in speaking; fluently

_____18. connived   r. sudden, impulsive action

Name _____

Schooner

Teacher Directions: Place students in small groups. Assign each group 4 or 5 sailing terms.

Group Directions: For each word assigned to your group, define its location and function on a schooner. As a bonus activity, draw a schooner and label the parts. Select one member of the group to present your information to the class.

1. keel
2. stern
3. rudder
4. tiller
5. hatch
6. hold
7. bulkhead
8. captain's cabin
9. crew quarters
10. mainmast
11. foremast
12. mainsail
13. gaff
14. main topsail
15. fore boom
16. foresail
17. fore topsail
18. fore staysail
19. jib
20. flying jib
21. bowsprit
22. main deck
23. quarter deck

Clue Log

Directions: When you read something you think might be important later on, write it down. What clues does the author of *Treasure Island* give you about how to find the treasure?

Page	Clue (event or item)	Could Have Something To Do With

15

Story Map

Directions: Complete the story map below as you read *Treasure Island*.

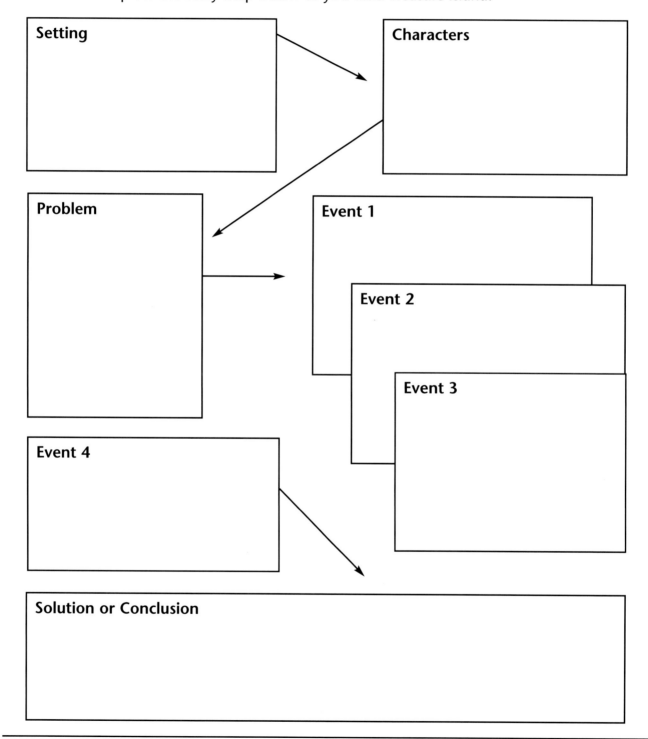

Setting

Characters

Problem

Event 1

Event 2

Event 3

Event 4

Solution or Conclusion

Character Attribute Chart

Directions: Choose at least five characters from the book. List their names in the left-hand boxes. Fill in the other boxes with the requested information.

Character	One-Word Description	Appearance	Significance to the Story	Do you know anyone similar?

Characters With Character

Directions: A person's **character** is evaluated by his or her actions, statements, and by the way he or she treats others. For each of the attributes listed in the center of the page, write the name of one character from the novel who has that trait, and the name of a character who does **not** have that trait. After each character's name, give an example of an action or statement which proves you have properly evaluated the character. Use a variety of characters as you fill out the chart.

Has This Trait		Doesn't Have This Trait
	tells the truth	
	keeps promises	
	considers consequences of actions	
	sacrifices for others	
	listens to others without pre-judging them	
	is a good person	
	is kind and caring	
	makes wise decisions	

Name _____

Conflict

The **conflict** of a story is the struggle between two people or two forces. There are three main types of conflict: person against person, person against nature or society, and person against himself/herself.

Directions: The characters in *Treasure Island* experience conflict in the story. In the chart below, list one of the conflicts each of the characters experienced, indicate what type of conflict it is, and explain how each conflict is resolved in the story.

Character: Jim Hawkins

Conflict	Resolution

Character: Ben Gunn

Conflict	Resolution

Character: Long John Silver

Conflict	Resolution

Jargon

When people use specific words particular to their occupation or environment, they are using **jargon**. *Treasure Island* is full of jargon associated with sailing, pirating, and even doctoring.

Directions: Make a list of at least ten words you find in *Treasure Island* that you would call "jargon." You may also include words that are rarely used today. Define and categorize the words to help you better understand the dialogue and description in the text.

Word or Phrase (Jargon)	Definition	Category
1. gentleman of fortune	common pirate	pirating
2. grog-shop	bar or tavern	pirating

Name _____

Leadership

Directions: Brainstorm the qualities that make a good leader on the attribute web below. Then, use the boxes to sort your ideas and relate them to different leaders in *Treasure Island*. Write a short essay explaining what you think makes a good leader and why, using examples from *Treasure Island* to support your claims.

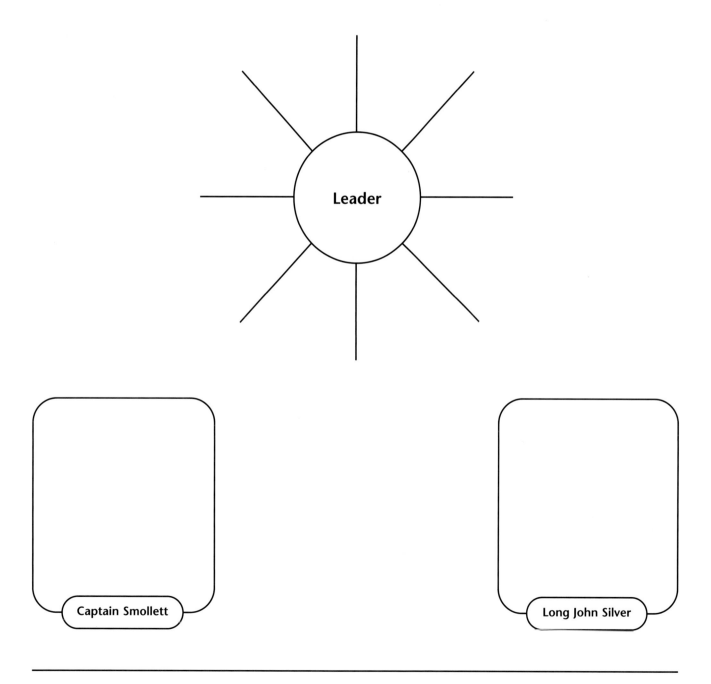

21

Cause/Effect

Directions: One way to map cause and effect is to look for an effect and then backtrack to the single or multiple causes. Think of one effect in the book and then brainstorm the causes for it.

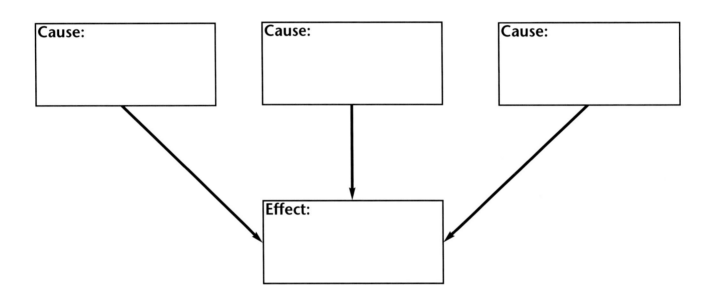

Directions: Many effects can be attributed to the actions of a single character. Choose one of the following prompts and write a short essay explaining how *Treasure Island* would be different if only one character was missing from the story.

    a. Suppose the *Hispaniola* sets sail for Treasure Island without the doctor on board. What are the major things that would change in the story? Will it end differently? Why or why not?

    b. What if the character of Ben Gunn doesn't exist? Tell how the story would be different and why.

    c. Suppose that Squire Trelawney does not say one word about treasure when he goes to buy a boat and get a crew ready. How would the story be different if only Dr. Livesey, Jim, and Trelawney know about Treasure Island?

Latitude and Longitude

Directions: Define the terms latitude and longitude. Then, using a world atlas, match the following places to the correct measure.

_____ 1. Australia

_____ 2. Atlantic Ocean

_____ 3. India

_____ 4. Europe

_____ 5. Brazil

_____ 6. Arctic Ocean

_____ 7. South Africa

_____ 8. Canada

_____ 9. Mexico

_____ 10. China

A. 50° North, 105° West

B. 15° North, 75° East

C. 30° South, 135° East

D. 15° South, 45° West

E. 80° North, 1° West

F. 45° North, 105° East

G. 45° North, 15° East

H. 30° North, 45° West

I. 20° North, 105° West

J. 30° South, 25° East

Directions: Mark each statement below as True (T) or False (F). If it is false, correct it so that it is true.

_____ 1. Captain Pew is the buccaneer who lodges at the Admiral Benbow.

_____

_____ 2. Jim Hawkins leaves his father and mother to go out in search of treasure.

_____

_____ 3. Squire Trelawney hires a one-legged man to be the cook for the voyage.

_____

_____ 4. The name of the ship the squire acquired is *Walrus*.

_____

_____ 5. Captain Smollett is very pleased with the crew Trelawney has chosen.

_____

_____ 6. Jim overhears a plan of mutiny, led by John Silver, while he is in the apple barrel.

_____

_____ 7. The nickname the crew gives John Silver is Barbecue.

_____

_____ 8. Jim goes to the island and runs into a dangerous animal in the woods.

_____

_____ 9. Jim sees Silver kill one of the honest men while on the island.

_____

_____10. Ben Gunn was marooned on the island three years before the *Hispaniola* arrives.

_____

Directions: List the pros and cons of Jim's decision to leave the block house to find Ben Gunn's boat. Then, on the lines below, write whether or not you agree with his decision and why. Give specific examples from the book to support your position.

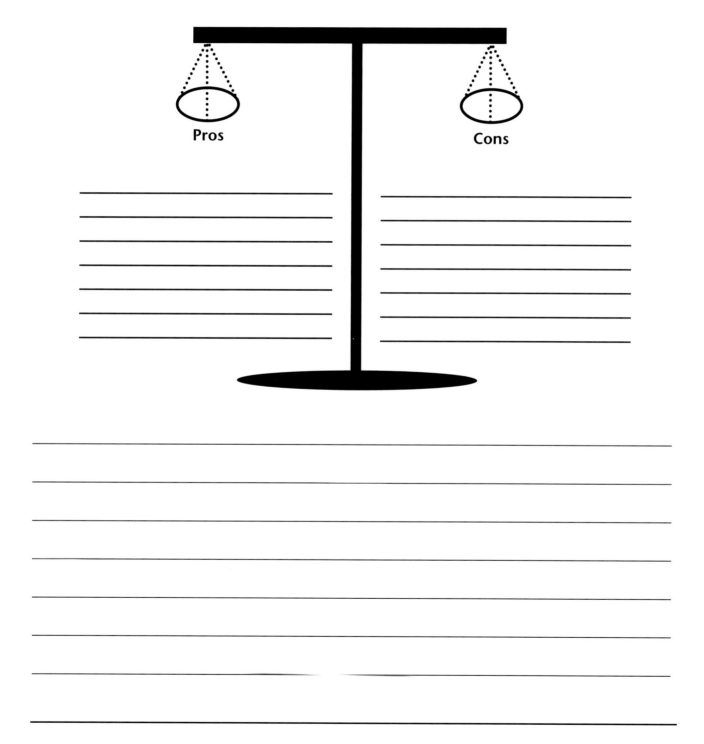

Pros   Cons

_____   _____

_____   _____

_____   _____

_____   _____

_____   _____

_____   _____

_____

_____

_____

_____

_____

_____

_____

Name _____

Quotations: Match the name of the character to the correct quotation. You may use some names more than once or not at all. (2 points each)

A. Jim Hawkins   B. Long John Silver   C. Squire Trelawney
D. Dr. Livesey   E. Jim's mother   F. Captain Flint
G. Captain Smollett   H. Israel Hands   I. Billy Bones
J. Ben Gunn

_____ 1. "You have been drinking rum; you have had a stroke, precisely as I told you..."

_____ 2. "I'll have my dues, and not a farthing over. Hold Mrs. Crossley's bag."

_____ 3. "Well, sir, better speak plain, I believe, even at the risk of offence. I don't like this cruise; I don't like the men; and I don't like my officer."

_____ 4. "Here's Cap'n Flint—I calls my parrot Cap'n Flint, after the famous buccaneer— here's Cap'n Flint predicting success to our v'yage. Wasn't you, cap'n?"

_____ 5. "Doctor, let me speak. Get the captain and squire down to the cabin, and then make some pretence to send for me. I have terrible news."

_____ 6. "I don't know about treasure, but I'll stake my wig there's fever here."

_____ 7. "You can kill the body...but not the spirit..."

_____ 8. "Him as strikes first is my fancy; dead men don't bite; them's my views—amen, so be it."

_____ 9. "Pieces of eight! Pieces of eight!"

_____10. "You give us the chart to get the treasure by, and drop shooting poor seamen and stoving of their heads in while asleep. You do that, and we'll offer you a choice."

Multiple Choice: Circle the BEST answer for each question. (2 points each)

1. The Admiral Benbow is
   A. Jim's father's inn
   B. the name of an abandoned ship
   C. a restaurant
   D. a man who is in charge of a pirate ship

2. The story is narrated by
   A. Jim and Dr. Livesey
   B. Jim
   C. Robert Louis Stevenson
   D. Jim and John Silver

3. Jim and his mother take an oilskin pouch from the chest of their lodger,
   A. Black Dog
   B. Billy Bones
   C. Pew
   D. Captain Flint

4. _____ dies after being trampled by horses.
   A. one of Jim's neighbors
   B. Dr. Livesey
   C. Black Dog
   D. Pew

5. The name of the ship Trelawney buys for the cruise is
   A. *Walrus*
   B. *Cassandra*
   C. *Hispaniola*
   D. none of the above

6. Everyone first believes that John Silver is
   A. another dishonest hand
   B. one of the few good men aboard
   C. an excellent cook
   D. a pirate

7. Captain Smollett's attitude about the cruise before it leaves is

    A. concerned
    B. content
    C. curious
    D. callous

8. The stern of a ship is located

    A. underneath the deck
    B. by the kitchen
    C. in the back
    D. in the front

9. Ben Gunn is on the island because he

    A. was shipwrecked there
    B. wanted to find Flint's treasure
    C. is a savage
    D. was marooned there

10. A gig is

    A. a musical instrument
    B. a chest for carrying items
    C. a small boat
    D. a pool of calm water

11. Israel Hands is

    A. Captain Smollett's mate
    B. Flint's old gunner
    C. one of the honest hands
    D. Long John's enemy

12. Dr. Livesey gives Long John the map to the treasure because

    A. he is tired of fighting to keep it
    B. he is trying to save Jim's life
    C. Ben Gunn already found and moved the treasure
    D. none of the above

Name _____

13. The night that Jim sneaks out of the block house,

  A. he tries to attack the pirates' camp
  B. he takes control of the *Hispaniola*
  C. he runs into Ben Gunn
  D. he tries to find the treasure himself

14. Long John Silver is

  A. two-faced
  B. selfless
  C. dumb
  D. loyal

15. When the men sailed for home with the treasure, they left behind

  A. Ben Gunn
  B. three of Silver's men
  C. Long John Silver
  D. no one

Fill-ins: Fill in the blanks below. (2 points each)

1. Jim overhears the mutineer's plan to take over the boat while he is in _____.

2. Long John Silver is also called _____ by the men.

3. _____ tries to kill Jim while he is on a ship.

4. _____ is the blind beggar.

5. They are searching for a treasure that was buried by _____.

6. _____ is an unexpected help on the island.

7. _____ is the first to find the treasure.

8. The author of *Treasure Island* is _____.

9. The country in which *Treasure Island* is set is _____.

10. The story is written in _____ point of view.

Essay: Choose one of the following to answer. (20 points)

1. Write an analysis of *Treasure Island* that includes the following: a discussion of the major theme, what you believe was the author's goal in writing it, and whether or not you think the author achieved his goal and why.

2. Write an essay explaining how Jim matures through the course of the novel. How is he different at the end as compared to the beginning? What events cause him to grow in maturity? Use specific examples from the book in your analysis.

Creative Writing: Choose one of the following to answer. (10 points)

1. Write the words to a song that you would sing if you were at sea on a treasure hunt. Try to include sailor or pirate jargon in the song.

2. How would the story be different if it was written from Long John Silver's point of view? Choose one section of the book that you remember well and rewrite it from Silver's perspective.

© Novel Units, Inc.

30

Answer Key

Activities #1–#2: Answers will vary.

Part One, "The Old Buccaneer," pp. 11-46

1. Admiral Benbow inn 2. It is lonely and well spoken of. 3. to keep an eye out for a seaman with only one leg 4. They are frightened by the content and aghast at the language, but still excited about hearing the adventures. 5. is not afraid of him at all; warns the guest not to threaten him or he will be punished by hanging 6. says he likes the boy, but orders him into the house so he can surprise the captain; then makes the boy leave so he can talk alone with the captain 7. The two men get into a fight; Black Dog leaves wounded and Billy Bones falls on the floor, apparently wounded. The doctor says he has had a stroke. 8. that he has something important in his chest and he wants the doctor to come and protect him from others who will come to get it; give him rum and get the doctor 9. receiving the black spot, which is a summons 10. Jim's father dies and everyone must make arrangements for a funeral. 11. a blind man who demands Jim take him to the captain 12. a piece of paper with a black spot that gives the captain six hours to live 13. dies; Jim begins to cry. He has only known two people who have died and is still mourning the loss of his father. 14. They go to the hamlet to ask for help defending the inn. With no help, they return to the inn and search the captain's chest for treasure, and find nothing but a bag of coins from which they take what they are owed. 15. the blind man; They leave with the money Jim's mother has counted and an oilskin bag to "square the count." 16. A group of buccaneers come to find Flint's fist among the captain's things after they learn is already dead. They do not find what they are looking for, and after hearing several warning signs, flee. Pew, the blind man, is left alone and trampled by charging horses after moving in the opposite direction of his ship. 17. the messenger to Dr. Livesey, Supervisor Dance, and some of his men 18. The doctor is a magistrate and can safely keep whatever Jim took from the captain that is of great value. 19. a book and a paper—a treasure map 20. They decide to get a ship and sail to the treasure. The doctor is worried that Trelawney will not keep the treasure hunt a secret.

Part Two, "The Sea-cook," pp. 47-80

1. what it is like to explore the island on the map 2. He has told many in Bristol about their adventure, has purchased a ship, and is readying a crew. He is particularly pleased with his choice of a cook, a one-legged man, who knows the sea well and gathered other well-skilled seamen to join the crew. Trelawney summons the doctor and Jim to come soon, allowing Jim to stay one night with his mother first. 3. Besides being excited about his coming adventure, he is sad to be leaving his mother and somewhat jealous of the apprentice who will help her run the inn in his absence. 4. At first, he was afraid it was the same man the captain had paid him to look out for. After meeting him and seeing Black Dog, his suspicions are raised again. But Long John's cleverness outwits Jim, and he comes to believe that the one-legged man is honest and innocent of knowing the buccaneers who searched the inn. 5. that he doesn't like the crew or the fact that the voyage is a search for treasure; He demands that things (gun powder, etc.) on the ship be rearranged and wants only a few people to ever see or know where the map is. The doctor suspects that there are only two honest men aboard—Captain Smollett and Long John. 6. They don't like the captain and think he is overly harsh. 7. Arrow, who always found a way to be drunk, disappeared one night and was said to have fallen overboard. Job Anderson, Trelawney, and Israel Hands (a close confidant of Silver's) help fill the position of mate, vacant after Arrow's death. 8. Many of the ship's hands gather to hear Long John tell stories about a past voyage. Jim discovers that Long John (who sailed with Flint himself) and many others are pirates planning a mutiny. He also realizes that they are convincing the honest hands on the ship to join them in their plans to take the treasure once it is found. It is clear that Long John is

---

their leader; it is he who decides that all of the honest men aboard will be killed as soon as the treasure is found. 9. the sight of land 10. He requests to speak with Dr. Livesey, Squire Trelawney, and Captain Smollett. 11. They will not do any harm to anyone until they know who are the honest hands and who are not. 12. Jim is told to be observant—his favor with the men may make them relaxed enough around him that Jim will be able to tell who is honest and who is not.

Part Three, "My Shore Adventure," pp. 81-90
1. They become less disciplined and more anxious. 2. Because the men are so agitated, Captain Smollett is fearful of making more demands of them. If he does not order them as usual, they will suspect something. They decide to let Long John take a few men ashore for a while. They are sure that Silver can tame his own men and keep them on task and in order as it is in his own best interest. 3. Six men are left aboard and thirteen, including Silver, go ashore. At the last minute, Jim slips into one of the gigs heading for land. When he docks, he immediately runs into the brush while Silver calls his name from behind. 4. He feels like he should try to listen in on the councils between Long John and the other men. 5. There is a loud cry. Someone has killed Alan, who was evidently one of the honest hands. 6. He takes a tree branch and throws it into Tom's back, knocking him over. He then kills Tom by stabbing him twice because he would not consent to follow the mutineers. 7. Jim is terrified and runs deeper into the woods until he fears he is lost. He thinks he may be the next to die. 8. a man named Ben Gunn who was left on the island three years before 9. Ben mentions Flint's name and asks whether or not the ship belongs to Flint. 10. the nature of the squire of the ship, whether or not they will take him home, and if they will let him keep some of the treasure if he helps them 11. the sound of cannons and guns from the shore

Part Four, "The Stockade," pp. 99-130
1. Dr. Livesey; Answers will vary. 2. that it is filled with disease and fever 3. take a gig and go ashore for information 4. He hears a man at the point of death and returns to the ship. He learns from Captain Smollett that one of the six left behind was not always a pirate and may be persuaded to join them. 5. move their provisions to the land and leave the boat barren for the pirates 6. weapons, food, a mattress for protection, and the doctor's medicine chest 7. the gun on the ship's stern and the round-shot it requires as ammunition 8. Israel Hands 9. It sinks because it is overloaded and the men are rushing to shore to escape the pirates and the ship's gun; Three guns and half of their powder and provisions sink into the water. 10. Tom Redruth, the older man left behind to guard the provisions in the gallery; He is cried over, prayed with, and then covered with a flag after his passing. 11. very little; The ship must aim so high that the balls hit the floor and do not ricochet or cause harm. 12. Ben Gunn sees the flag they raise over the stockade and convinces Jim it is his friends, otherwise the flag would be the Jolly Roger. 13. the black flag of piracy, usually marked with a skull and crossbones 14. poor; One man is lost, the rations are scarce, and they have no access to the *Hispaniola*; however, their enemy camp's climate and the buccaneers' drinking rum is in their favor. 15. Two men gather firewood, two dig a grave for Redruth, the doctor is the cook, Jim is the sentry at the door, and the captain helps all; They decide they must kill the buccaneers until they surrender or leave in the ship. 16. cautiously; He orders each man to take a certain post and watch for a sudden attack; he allows Silver to talk and promises he and his men will not attack him unfairly. 17. Someone snuck into the buccaneer camp the night before and killed a man with a hand spike. Jim thinks it was Ben Gunn, which is why the captain doesn't understand what Silver is talking about. 18. Silver wants the captain to hand over the treasure map in exchange for part of the treasure and a ride home, or the freedom to stay on the island with part of the treasure and wait for Silver to send the next ship he finds to rescue them. The captain refuses; Answers will vary. 19. that each man must come before the captain unarmed and be put in chains and taken back to England for a fair trial; Silver refuses.

20. None of the men are at their post when he returns from his conversation with Silver. 21. the north side of the stockade 22. four (Captain's men) to nine (Silver's men); Note the footnote which numbers Silver's men at eight. 23. Answers will vary.

Part Five, "My Sea Adventure," pp. 131-166
1. The doctor cares for them. Hunter and a pirate die quickly; Captain Smollett survives the wound. 2. to see Ben Gunn 3. sneak out of the stockade and climb to the white rock to get the boat made by Ben Gunn; row to the *Hispaniola* and cut it loose from its anchor 4. the type of boat made by Ben Gunn that Jim uses to get to the *Hispaniola*; The boat is small and hard to steer, preferring to go in circles rather than a straight line; Jim has difficulty keeping it on course and eventually has to allow the current of the water to guide it. 5. Israel Hands and the man in the red cap 6. yes; He cuts the boat loose and then decides to climb aboard. 7. The man in the red cap is dead and Israel Hands is wounded and drunk. 8. that he has taken over the ship and is now captain; removes the Jolly Roger 9. If Jim lets Hands live, gets him food, drink, and a bandage for his leg, then Hands will tell Jim how to sail the ship to the North Inlet. 10. wine from below 11. that Hands can walk and that he retrieved a long knife with which to kill Jim when Jim returns from below 12. He claims that it will probably be his last because he thinks he is close to death. 13. Jim thinks you can kill the body but not the spirit. Israel Hands isn't afraid of spirits and only knows that "dead men don't bite." 14. Sea water spoiled it and he had not yet reloaded. 15. throws it at him and pins him to the mast 16. Jim shoots Israel Hands and Hands falls into the sea. 17. He is unemotional; Jim's "tragical adventure" have made him less afraid of the dead. 18. As he approaches the stockade, he sees the remains of a large fire. The men did not have much firewood, nor did they like to make such large fires. 19. Captain Flint, Silver's parrot 20. Answers will vary.

Part Six, "Captain Silver," pp. 167-211
1. six 2. that they are still alive, but want nothing to do with him since he deserted them; Answers will vary. 3. why Long John and his men are in the stockade and where his friends are; Long John reveals that the doctor came to make a pact when they discovered the ship was gone. Long John and his men got the bunker and many supplies while the remaining four left alive. 4. Jim is courageous as he reveals how he is the one who found out about the mutineers and the one who took over the boat. He declares he is not afraid of them and they can kill him if they want, but that he will spare them from the gallows if they let him live. 5. Tom Morgan; Long John rebukes him. 6. hold a council; yes 7. that he is now on the squire's side, that he will save Jim if Jim will stick by him, and that the doctor gave him the treasure map 8. the black spot; the cover of Dick's Bible 9. The recipient must receive it, turn it over, and see what is written. The givers must list their grievances and then the recipient, as captain, replies to the charges and the deposition. 10. He's bungled the cruise, let the enemy out of the stockade without making them pay a price, let his crew march after the enemy, and then refused to let his men kill the boy. 11. Long John tells the crew that it was the crew and the captain who "made a hash" of the cruise. He claims that he let the enemy out because of the value of having a doctor come to them daily to help them overcome their sicknesses and wounds. He does not want to kill Jim because he is a viable hostage, and shows that they didn't need to follow after the enemy because they left him the treasure map. The crew renegotiates its previous summons and again declares Long John the captain. 12. He treats them as regular patients and is calm and laid back, and they respond as if he still is the ship's doctor. 13. They think Silver is playing double—trying to save himself even if it means sacrificing them later on; Yes, even Jim sees how clearly Silver is trying to make peace with both sides so that he is sure to come off of the island safely. 14. The doctor reprimands him for leaving the block house, Jim is sorrowful, and the doctor tells him to come with him. Jim refuses because he gave his word to Silver, but tells the doctor what happened when he left

and where the ship is in case he is tortured and forced to tell the mutineers of its location. The doctor is pleased and lists all of the things Jim has done to save them. 15. that he will do what he can to keep him from punishment in England, look out for squalls when finding treasure, and keep the boy close and call out when he needs help 16. Answers may vary but should include that he wants to save Jim. 17. those they let leave have the ship and finding out that key information is why he let Jim talk to the doctor; he claims that they will find the ship after they find the treasure and then have the upper hand. 18. uneasy about Silver's constant shifting of sides and a wariness of seeking treasure because of what the doctor warned Silver about 19. a tall tree 20. the skeleton of a dead man, stripped of anything valuable and positioned in an unnatural way; It is positioned unnaturally because it is pointing toward the treasure. 21. Flint's ghost; Ben Gunn 22. They discover someone else has already found and taken the treasure. 23. Ben Gunn found it months before and moved it to another location. 24. take the treasure to the *Hispaniola*; leave the three men on the island with provisions for fear of more problems on the voyage home 25. He takes a bag of coins from the treasure and leaves the crew when they stop to get fresh hands for the voyage home. 26. Smollett retires from the sea; Gunn uses his treasure quickly and goes back to begging; Gray saves his money, goes to school, and starts a family.

Activity #3: 1. gears 2. year of mercy 3. hurry 4. vibrant 5. tearoom 6. scrupulous 7. gallows 8. jewelry 9. grip 10. cleared 11. caress 12. recorded 13. illegitimate 14. proudly 15. left-hook 16. stormed 17. understandable

Activity #4: Word maps will vary.

Activity #5:

34

Activity #6: 1. m 2. i 3. b 4. r 5. o 6. j 7. d 8. k 9. c 10. p 11. h 12. a 13. f 14. n 15. q 16. e 17. l 18. g

Activities #7-#15: Answers will vary.

Activity #16: 1. C 2. H 3. B 4. G 5. D 6. E 7. J 8. A 9. I 10. F

Comprehension Quiz #1

1. F—Captain Billy Bones is the lodger. 2. F—His father already passed away. 3. T 4. F—*Hispaniola*; *Walrus* was Flint's ship. 5. F—not pleased 6. T 7. T 8. F—He runs into Ben Gunn. 9. T 10. T

Comprehension Quiz #2

Answers will vary, but should be thoughtful and well-reasoned. Answers should include: Pros—finds Ben's boat and takes over the *Hispaniola*, ultimately allowing him and his friends to take the treasure and leave the island; Cons—friends do not know where he is, is almost killed by Israel Hands, returns to the block house where Silver's men take him hostage

Novel Test

Quotations: 1. D (p. 22) 2. E (p. 33) 3. G (p. 59) 4. B (p. 66) 5. A (p. 77) 6. D (p. 83) 7. A (p. 153) 8. H (p. 156) 9. F (p. 166) 10. B (p. 123)

Multiple Choice: 1. A 2. A 3. B 4. D 5. C 6. B 7. A 8. C 9. D 10. C 11. B 12. C 13. B 14. A 15. B

Fill-ins: 1. the apple barrel (or galley) 2. Barbecue 3. Israel Hands 4. Pew 5. Captain Flint 6. Ben Gunn 7. Ben Gunn 8. Robert Louis Stevenson 9. Great Britain (or England) 10. first-person

Essay: Answers will vary, but suggested answers follow. Besides accurate information, essays should be graded on grammar use and effective organization. Each essay should answer all parts of the question chosen.

1. Major theme: good vs. evil, as evidenced by characters, setting, and events; Author's goal: writing an adventure story with great appeal, pleasing to himself and his father, as evidenced within the text and in supplementary material in the book; Goal achieved: yes, as evidenced by the book's enduring popularity

2. Jim initially appears fearful, naïve, clever, and scared in the beginning when he: does not like to oppose or offend Billy Bones; cries over the death of his father and Billy Bones; is easily duped by Silver; is wise about calling on the doctor when finding the pouch in Billy Bones' chest. As the story progresses, he grows in boldness, leaving the ship with the other sixteen men, facing Ben Gunn, fighting the pirates, taking over the ship, killing Hands and pushing another dead man overboard, and making deals with Silver. Death no longer affects him and pirates no longer scare him the way they once did.

Creative Writing: Answers will vary. Grade responses based on their creativity, use of learned information (jargon, etc.), and critical thinking.

Notes